This book belongs to:

D1416319

Location:

DATE:

N
W E
S

WEATHER:

TODAYS ACTIVITY:

THE MOST INTERESTING I SAW:

TODAY I ATE:

TODAY I LEARNED:

Sketch what you saw:

RATE YOUR DAY:     

TODAY'S FAVORITE MEMORY:

TODAY I AM GRATEFUL FOR:

Location:

DATE:

N
W E
S

WEATHER:

TODAYS ACTIVITY:

THE MOST INTERESTING I SAW:

TODAY I ATE:

TODAY I LEARNED:

Sketch what you saw:

RATE YOUR DAY:     

TODAY'S FAVORITE MEMORY:

TODAY I AM GRATEFUL FOR:

Location:

DATE:

N
W E
S

WEATHER:

TODAYS ACTIVITY:

THE MOST INTERESTING I SAW:

TODAY I ATE:

TODAY I LEARNED:

Sketch what you saw:

RATE YOUR DAY:     

TODAY'S FAVORITE MEMORY:

TODAY I AM GRATEFUL FOR:

Location:

DATE:

N
W E
S

WEATHER:

TODAYS ACTIVITY:

THE MOST INTERESTING I SAW:

TODAY I ATE:

TODAY I LEARNED:

Sketch what you saw:

RATE YOUR DAY:     

TODAY'S FAVORITE MEMORY:

TODAY I AM GRATEFUL FOR:

Location:

N

W E

S

DATE:

WEATHER:

TODAYS ACTIVITY:

THE MOST INTERESTING I SAW:

TODAY I ATE:

TODAY I LEARNED:

Sketch what you saw:

RATE YOUR DAY:     

TODAY'S FAVORITE MEMORY:

TODAY I AM GRATEFUL FOR:

Location:

DATE:

N

W E

S

WEATHER:

TODAYS ACTIVITY:

THE MOST INTERESTING I SAW:

TODAY I ATE:

TODAY I LEARNED:

Sketch what you saw:

RATE YOUR DAY:    

TODAY'S FAVORITE MEMORY:

TODAY I AM GRATEFUL FOR:

Location:

DATE:

WEATHER:

TODAYS ACTIVITY:

THE MOST INTERESTING I SAW:

TODAY I ATE:

TODAY I LEARNED:

Sketch what you saw:

RATE YOUR DAY:    

TODAY'S FAVORITE MEMORY:

TODAY I AM GRATEFUL FOR:

Location:

DATE:

N

W E

S

WEATHER:

TODAYS ACTIVITY:

THE MOST INTERESTING I SAW:

TODAY I ATE:

TODAY I LEARNED:

Sketch what you saw:

RATE YOUR DAY:     

TODAY'S FAVORITE MEMORY:

TODAY I AM GRATEFUL FOR:

Location:

DATE:

N
W E
S

WEATHER:

TODAYS ACTIVITY:

THE MOST INTERESTING I SAW:

TODAY I ATE:

TODAY I LEARNED:

Sketch what you saw:

RATE YOUR DAY:     

TODAY'S FAVORITE MEMORY:

TODAY I AM GRATEFUL FOR:

Location:

DATE:

N W E S

WEATHER:

TODAYS ACTIVITY:

THE MOST INTERESTING I SAW:

TODAY I ATE:

TODAY I LEARNED:

Sketch what you saw:

RATE YOUR DAY:     

TODAY'S FAVORITE MEMORY:

TODAY I AM GRATEFUL FOR:

Location:

DATE:

WEATHER:

TODAYS ACTIVITY:

THE MOST INTERESTING I SAW:

TODAY I ATE:

TODAY I LEARNED:

Sketch what you saw:

RATE YOUR DAY:     

TODAY'S FAVORITE MEMORY:

TODAY I AM GRATEFUL FOR:

Location:

DATE:

N
W E
S

WEATHER:

TODAYS ACTIVITY:

THE MOST INTERESTING I SAW:

TODAY I ATE:

TODAY I LEARNED:

Sketch what you saw:

RATE YOUR DAY:     

TODAY'S FAVORITE MEMORY:

TODAY I AM GRATEFUL FOR:

Location:

DATE:

N W E S

WEATHER:

TODAYS ACTIVITY:

THE MOST INTERESTING I SAW:

TODAY I ATE:

TODAY I LEARNED:

Sketch what you saw:

RATE YOUR DAY:     

TODAY'S FAVORITE MEMORY:

TODAY I AM GRATEFUL FOR:

Location:

N W E S

DATE:

WEATHER:

TODAYS ACTIVITY:

THE MOST INTERESTING I SAW:

TODAY I ATE:

TODAY I LEARNED:

Sketch what you saw:

RATE YOUR DAY:     

TODAY'S FAVORITE MEMORY:

TODAY I AM GRATEFUL FOR:

Location:

N

W E

S

DATE:

WEATHER:

TODAYS ACTIVITY:

THE MOST INTERESTING I SAW:

TODAY I ATE:

TODAY I LEARNED:

Sketch what you saw:

RATE YOUR DAY:     

TODAY'S FAVORITE MEMORY:

TODAY I AM GRATEFUL FOR:

Location:

N
W E
S

DATE:

WEATHER:

TODAYS ACTIVITY:

THE MOST INTERESTING I SAW:

TODAY I ATE:

TODAY I LEARNED:

Sketch what you saw:

RATE YOUR DAY:    

TODAY'S FAVORITE MEMORY:

TODAY I AM GRATEFUL FOR:

Location:

DATE:

WEATHER:

TODAYS ACTIVITY:

THE MOST INTERESTING I SAW:

TODAY I ATE:

TODAY I LEARNED:

Sketch what you saw:

RATE YOUR DAY:     

TODAY'S FAVORITE MEMORY:

TODAY I AM GRATEFUL FOR:

Location:

DATE:

N W E S

WEATHER:

TODAYS ACTIVITY:

THE MOST INTERESTING I SAW:

TODAY I ATE:

TODAY I LEARNED:

Sketch what you saw:

RATE YOUR DAY:     

TODAY'S FAVORITE MEMORY:

TODAY I AM GRATEFUL FOR:

Location:

N
W E
S

DATE:

WEATHER:

TODAYS ACTIVITY:

THE MOST INTERESTING I SAW:

TODAY I ATE:

TODAY I LEARNED:

Sketch what you saw:

RATE YOUR DAY:     

TODAY'S FAVORITE MEMORY:

TODAY I AM GRATEFUL FOR:

Location:

N

W E

S

DATE:

WEATHER:

TODAYS ACTIVITY:

THE MOST INTERESTING I SAW:

TODAY I ATE:

TODAY I LEARNED:

Sketch what you saw:

RATE YOUR DAY:     

TODAY'S FAVORITE MEMORY:

TODAY I AM GRATEFUL FOR:

Location:

N

W E

S

DATE:

WEATHER:

TODAYS ACTIVITY:

THE MOST INTERESTING I SAW:

TODAY I ATE:

TODAY I LEARNED:

Sketch what you saw:

RATE YOUR DAY:     

TODAY'S FAVORITE MEMORY:

TODAY I AM GRATEFUL FOR:

Location:

N
W E
S

DATE:

WEATHER:

TODAYS ACTIVITY:

THE MOST INTERESTING I SAW:

TODAY I ATE:

TODAY I LEARNED:

Sketch what you saw:

RATE YOUR DAY:     

TODAY'S FAVORITE MEMORY:

TODAY I AM GRATEFUL FOR:

Location:

DATE:

WEATHER:

TODAYS ACTIVITY:

THE MOST INTERESTING I SAW:

TODAY I ATE:

TODAY I LEARNED:

Sketch what you saw:

RATE YOUR DAY:     

TODAY'S FAVORITE MEMORY:

TODAY I AM GRATEFUL FOR:

Location:

N
W E
S

DATE:

WEATHER:

TODAYS ACTIVITY:

THE MOST INTERESTING I SAW:

TODAY I ATE:

TODAY I LEARNED:

Sketch what you saw:

RATE YOUR DAY:     

TODAY'S FAVORITE MEMORY:

TODAY I AM GRATEFUL FOR:

Location:

DATE:

WEATHER:

N
W E
S

TODAYS ACTIVITY:

THE MOST INTERESTING I SAW:

TODAY I ATE:

TODAY I LEARNED:

Sketch what you saw:

RATE YOUR DAY:     

TODAY'S FAVORITE MEMORY:

TODAY I AM GRATEFUL FOR:

Location:

DATE:

N
W E
S

WEATHER:

TODAYS ACTIVITY:

THE MOST INTERESTING I SAW:

TODAY I ATE:

TODAY I LEARNED:

Sketch what you saw:

RATE YOUR DAY:     

TODAY'S FAVORITE MEMORY:

TODAY I AM GRATEFUL FOR:

Location:

N
W E
S

DATE:

WEATHER:

TODAYS ACTIVITY:

THE MOST INTERESTING I SAW:

TODAY I ATE:

TODAY I LEARNED:

Sketch what you saw:

RATE YOUR DAY:     

TODAY'S FAVORITE MEMORY:

TODAY I AM GRATEFUL FOR:

Location:

N
W E
S

DATE:

WEATHER:

TODAYS ACTIVITY:

THE MOST INTERESTING I SAW:

TODAY I ATE:

TODAY I LEARNED:

Sketch what you saw:

RATE YOUR DAY:     

TODAY'S FAVORITE MEMORY:

TODAY I AM GRATEFUL FOR:

Location:

N
W E
S

DATE:

WEATHER:

TODAYS ACTIVITY:

THE MOST INTERESTING I SAW:

TODAY I ATE:

TODAY I LEARNED:

Sketch what you saw:

RATE YOUR DAY:     

TODAY'S FAVORITE MEMORY:

TODAY I AM GRATEFUL FOR:

Location:

DATE:

N
W E
S

WEATHER:

TODAYS ACTIVITY:

THE MOST INTERESTING I SAW:

TODAY I ATE:

TODAY I LEARNED:

Sketch what you saw:

RATE YOUR DAY:     

TODAY'S FAVORITE MEMORY:

TODAY I AM GRATEFUL FOR:

Location:

DATE:

WEATHER:

TODAYS ACTIVITY:

THE MOST INTERESTING I SAW:

TODAY I ATE:

TODAY I LEARNED:

Sketch what you saw:

RATE YOUR DAY:     

TODAY'S FAVORITE MEMORY:

TODAY I AM GRATEFUL FOR:

Location:

N W E S

DATE:

WEATHER:

TODAYS ACTIVITY:

THE MOST INTERESTING I SAW:

TODAY I ATE:

TODAY I LEARNED:

Sketch what you saw:

RATE YOUR DAY:     

TODAY'S FAVORITE MEMORY:

TODAY I AM GRATEFUL FOR:

Location:

N
W E
S

DATE:

WEATHER:

TODAYS ACTIVITY:

THE MOST INTERESTING I SAW:

TODAY I ATE:

TODAY I LEARNED:

Sketch what you saw:

RATE YOUR DAY:     

TODAY'S FAVORITE MEMORY:

TODAY I AM GRATEFUL FOR:

Location:

DATE:

N
W E
S

WEATHER:

TODAYS ACTIVITY:

THE MOST INTERESTING I SAW:

TODAY I ATE:

TODAY I LEARNED:

Sketch what you saw:

RATE YOUR DAY:     

TODAY'S FAVORITE MEMORY:

TODAY I AM GRATEFUL FOR:

Location:

DATE:

N W E S

WEATHER:

TODAYS ACTIVITY:

THE MOST INTERESTING I SAW:

TODAY I ATE:

TODAY I LEARNED:

Sketch what you saw:

RATE YOUR DAY:     

TODAY'S FAVORITE MEMORY:

TODAY I AM GRATEFUL FOR:

Location:

DATE:

N
W E
S

WEATHER:

TODAYS ACTIVITY:

THE MOST INTERESTING I SAW:

TODAY I ATE:

TODAY I LEARNED:

Sketch what you saw:

RATE YOUR DAY:     

TODAY'S FAVORITE MEMORY:

TODAY I AM GRATEFUL FOR:

Location:

DATE:

N
W E
S

WEATHER:

TODAYS ACTIVITY:

THE MOST INTERESTING I SAW:

TODAY I ATE:

TODAY I LEARNED:

Sketch what you saw:

RATE YOUR DAY:     

TODAY'S FAVORITE MEMORY:

TODAY I AM GRATEFUL FOR:

Location:

DATE:

N
W E
S

WEATHER:

TODAYS ACTIVITY:

THE MOST INTERESTING I SAW:

TODAY I ATE:

TODAY I LEARNED:

Sketch what you saw:

RATE YOUR DAY:     

TODAY'S FAVORITE MEMORY:

TODAY I AM GRATEFUL FOR:

Location:

N W E S

DATE:

WEATHER:

TODAYS ACTIVITY:

THE MOST INTERESTING I SAW:

TODAY I ATE:

TODAY I LEARNED:

Sketch what you saw:

RATE YOUR DAY:     

TODAY'S FAVORITE MEMORY:

TODAY I AM GRATEFUL FOR:

Location:

DATE:

N
W E
S

WEATHER:

TODAYS ACTIVITY:

THE MOST INTERESTING I SAW:

TODAY I ATE:

TODAY I LEARNED:

Sketch what you saw:

RATE YOUR DAY:     

TODAY'S FAVORITE MEMORY:

TODAY I AM GRATEFUL FOR:

Location:

N
W E
S

DATE:

WEATHER:

TODAYS ACTIVITY:

THE MOST INTERESTING I SAW:

TODAY I ATE:

TODAY I LEARNED:

Sketch what you saw:

RATE YOUR DAY:     

TODAY'S FAVORITE MEMORY:

TODAY I AM GRATEFUL FOR:

Location:

DATE:

N
W E
S

WEATHER:

TODAYS ACTIVITY:

THE MOST INTERESTING I SAW:

TODAY I ATE:

TODAY I LEARNED:

Sketch what you saw:

RATE YOUR DAY:     

TODAY'S FAVORITE MEMORY:

TODAY I AM GRATEFUL FOR:

Location:

N
W E
S

DATE:

WEATHER:

TODAYS ACTIVITY:

THE MOST INTERESTING I SAW:

TODAY I ATE:

TODAY I LEARNED:

Sketch what you saw:

RATE YOUR DAY:     

TODAY'S FAVORITE MEMORY:

TODAY I AM GRATEFUL FOR:

Location:

N
W
E
S

DATE:

WEATHER:

TODAYS ACTIVITY:

THE MOST INTERESTING I SAW:

TODAY I ATE:

TODAY I LEARNED:

Sketch what you saw:

RATE YOUR DAY:     

TODAY'S FAVORITE MEMORY:

TODAY I AM GRATEFUL FOR:

Location:

DATE:

WEATHER:

N

W E

S

TODAYS ACTIVITY:

THE MOST INTERESTING I SAW:

TODAY I ATE:

TODAY I LEARNED:

Sketch what you saw:

RATE YOUR DAY:    

TODAY'S FAVORITE MEMORY:

TODAY I AM GRATEFUL FOR:

Location:

DATE:

N
W E
S

WEATHER:

TODAYS ACTIVITY:

THE MOST INTERESTING I SAW:

TODAY I ATE:

TODAY I LEARNED:

Sketch what you saw:

RATE YOUR DAY:    

TODAY I AM GRATEFUL FOR:

Location:

DATE:

N
W E
S

WEATHER:

TODAYS ACTIVITY:

THE MOST INTERESTING I SAW:

TODAY I ATE:

TODAY I LEARNED:

Sketch what you saw:

RATE YOUR DAY:     

TODAY'S FAVORITE MEMORY:

TODAY I AM GRATEFUL FOR:

Location:

DATE:

N W E S

WEATHER:

TODAYS ACTIVITY:

THE MOST INTERESTING I SAW:

TODAY I ATE:

TODAY I LEARNED:

Sketch what you saw:

RATE YOUR DAY:     

TODAY'S FAVORITE MEMORY:

TODAY I AM GRATEFUL FOR:

Location:

N

W E

S

DATE:

WEATHER:

TODAYS ACTIVITY:

THE MOST INTERESTING I SAW:

TODAY I ATE:

TODAY I LEARNED:

Sketch what you saw:

RATE YOUR DAY:     

TODAY'S FAVORITE MEMORY:

TODAY I AM GRATEFUL FOR:

Location:

N
W E
S

DATE:

WEATHER:

TODAYS ACTIVITY:

THE MOST INTERESTING I SAW:

TODAY I ATE:

TODAY I LEARNED:

Sketch what you saw:

RATE YOUR DAY:    

TODAY'S FAVORITE MEMORY:

TODAY I AM GRATEFUL FOR:

Location:

DATE:

WEATHER:

N

W E

S

TODAYS ACTIVITY:

THE MOST INTERESTING I SAW:

TODAY I ATE:

TODAY I LEARNED:

Sketch what you saw:

RATE YOUR DAY:     

TODAY'S FAVORITE MEMORY:

TODAY I AM GRATEFUL FOR:

Location:

N
W E
S

DATE:

WEATHER:

TODAYS ACTIVITY:

THE MOST INTERESTING I SAW:

TODAY I ATE:

TODAY I LEARNED:

Sketch what you saw:

RATE YOUR DAY:     

TODAY'S FAVORITE MEMORY:

TODAY I AM GRATEFUL FOR:

Location:

DATE:

N

W E

S

WEATHER:

TODAYS ACTIVITY:

THE MOST INTERESTING I SAW:

TODAY I ATE:

TODAY I LEARNED:

Sketch what you saw:

RATE YOUR DAY:     

TODAY'S FAVORITE MEMORY:

TODAY I AM GRATEFUL FOR:

Location:

DATE:

N
W E
S

WEATHER:

TODAYS ACTIVITY:

THE MOST INTERESTING I SAW:

TODAY I ATE:

TODAY I LEARNED:

RATE YOUR DAY:     

TODAY'S FAVORITE MEMORY:

TODAY I AM GRATEFUL FOR:

Location:

DATE:

WEATHER:

TODAYS ACTIVITY:

THE MOST INTERESTING I SAW:

TODAY I ATE:

TODAY I LEARNED:

Sketch what you saw:

RATE YOUR DAY:     

TODAY'S FAVORITE MEMORY:

TODAY I AM GRATEFUL FOR: